C0001608&5

DARK
PEAK

CLASSIC LANDFORMS OF THE

DARK PEAK

ROGER DALTON, HOWARD FOX AND PETER JONES

University of Derby

Series editors

Rodney Castleden and Christopher Green

Published by the Geographical Association
in conjunction with the
British Geomorphological Research Group

THE GEOGRAPHICAL ASSOCIATION

THE BRITISH GEOMORPHOLOGICAL RESEARCH GROUP

PREFACE

Geomorphologists study landforms and the processes that create and modify them. The results of their work, published as they invariably are in specialist journals, usually remain inaccessible to the general public. We would like to put that right. Scattered across the landscapes of England and Wales there are many beautiful and striking landforms that delight the eye of the general public and are also visited by educational parties from schools, colleges and universities. Our aim in producing this series of guides is to make modern explanations of these classic landforms available to all, in a style and format that will be easy to use in the field. We hope that an informed understanding of the origins of the features will help the visitor to enjoy the landscape all the more.

Encouraged by the success of the first edition of the Classic Landform Guides we are pleased to introduce this new edition, enhanced by colour photographs, new illustrations and with the valuable addition of 1:50 000 map extracts by kind permission of the Education Team, Ordnance Survey. The relevant maps for the area covered in this book are: Ordnance Survey Maps 1:63 360 Peak District Tourist Map; 1:50 000 Landranger Series sheets, 110, 118 and 119, 1:25 000 Outdoor Leisure Maps sheet 1 (The Peak District – Dark Peak area) and sheet 24 (The Peak District – White Peak area). Please refer to the current Ordnance Survey Index for other 1:25 000 availability. The British Geological Survey also publishes a series of geological maps which complement much of the content of this book. They include the 1:25 000 sheets 18 (Roaches/Upper Dovedale), 19 (Buxton), 20 (Castleton) and 24 (Monyash) and the 1:50 000 sheets 99 (Chapel-en-le-Frith), 111 (Buxton) and 112 (Chesterfield).

Rodney Castleden *Roedean School, Brighton*
Christopher Green *Royal Holloway, University of London*

© the Geographical Association, 1990, 1999
As a benefit of membership, the Association allows its members
to reproduce material for their own internal school/departmental use,
provided that the copyright is held by the GA, and that the user acknowledges
the source. This waiver does not apply to Ordnance Survey mapping, questions
about which should be referred to the Ordnance Survey.
ISBN 1 899085 61 0
This edition first published 1999
Published by the Geographical Association, 160 Solly Street, Sheffield S1 4BF.
The views expressed in this publication are those of the authors and do not necessarily
represent those of the Geographical Association.
The Geographical Association is a registered charity no. 313129.
Cover photograph: Looking south across the Dark Peak from Derwent Edge.
Photo: Roger Dalton.
Frontispiece: Millstones below Stanage Edge. Photo: Peter Jones.

CONTENTS

Introduction   *6*

The Western Margins   *12*

The Goyt Valley   *14*

The Roaches   *17*

The Northern Margins   *22*

Edale and Kinder Scout   *24*

Mam Tor   *33*

The Eastern Margins   *36*

The Derwent Edges   *37*

Tors in the Hathersage Area   *41*

The Ashover Anticline   *46*

Glossary   *50*

Bibliography   *51*

Acknowledgements

The Geographical Association would like to thank the following organisations
for permission to reproduce material in this publication: The British Geological
Survey for the map of Edale at 1:50 000 scale on page 25, reproduced by permission
of the Director, BGS © NERC. All rights reserved.
Mapping reproduced from Ordnance Survey 1:50 000 Landranger mapping
with the permission of The Controller of The Stationery Office
© Crown Copyright 82324M 09/96.
Illustrations: Paul Coles
Series design concept: Quarto Design, Huddersfield
Design and typesetting: ATG Design Communication, Huddersfield
Printed and bound in Hong Kong by: Colorcraft Limited

INTRODUCTION

The Peak District (Figure 1) is a scenically attractive upland area some 1600km^2 in extent which forms the southern part of the Pennine upland. Its landscape qualities are reflected in its designation

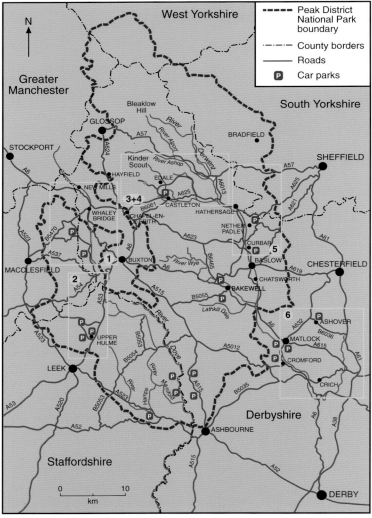

Figure 1: The Peak District: Location and access to the areas covered in this guide.

as a National Park. Geology is the basis for its division into sharply contrasting landscape types (Figure 2). The unroofing of the anticlinal Derbyshire Dome has revealed the Dinantian limestones at the core of the southern part of the District, the area known popularly as the White Peak (Dalton *et al.*, 1999). In contrast the areas which flank the White Peak to the east and west together with an extensive tract to the north are known as the Dark or High Peak. Here the geology is dominated by Namurian shales and sandstones. The term 'High' derives from the greater elevation of the Namurian **outcrop**, whereas 'Dark' may reflect the character of geology, soil and vegetation. The Namurian sandstones, when occurring as natural outcrops, stone wall material or building stone, weather to a dark grey while the acid, peaty moorlands characteristic of the uplands give rise to sombre tones. This guide is concerned with those parts of the Dark Peak which lie mainly within the counties of Derbyshire and Staffordshire.

Throughout the Dark Peak several major factors are fundamental to an understanding of landforms. These are **lithological** variations in the sequence of rocks, the presence of localised synclinal and anticlinal fold structures and the consequences of the variations in climate during the Pleistocene period. With respect to the last, the Devensian ice sheet reached the western margins of the Dark Peak while **periglacial** climates prevailed right across the area. The distribution of major elements of the geomorphology of the Dark Peak is summarised in Figure 3.

Lithological variations reflect the changing depositional environment which existed in Namurian times, characterised by rhythmic successions of deep-water fine sediment and shallow-water deltaic conditions. Sequences commonly pass upwards from fine-grained deep-water sediments, i.e. shales and mudstones, to deltaic sandstones of variable coarseness. Mudstones and shales, such as the Edale Shales, are more common in the Lower Namurian while sandstones occur more frequently in the upper sequences of the formation as deltaic conditions became more frequent. As deltas differed in extent, so the sandstones vary in thickness and spatial development showing a marked tendency to thin or wedge out laterally. The overall thickness of the Namurian strata varies. Conditions on the eastern margins were more stable than elsewhere in the Dark Peak with the result that some 300m of deposits occur in the vicinity of Chatsworth Park. This compares with 1000m at Kinder Low in the north and 1100m in the western margins between Glossop and Leek.

The significance of the lithological variation lies in the strongly developed **differential erosion** of the weaker shales and mudstones as opposed to the grits and sandstones. The latter give rise to scarps and associated **free faces** or edges which may be fashioned into **tor**-like features and fringed with accumulations of weathered debris. Such landforms are numerous throughout the Dark Peak and those in the Hathersage Moor area may be taken as representative. The sequence of strata also gives rise to slope instability. Not infrequently

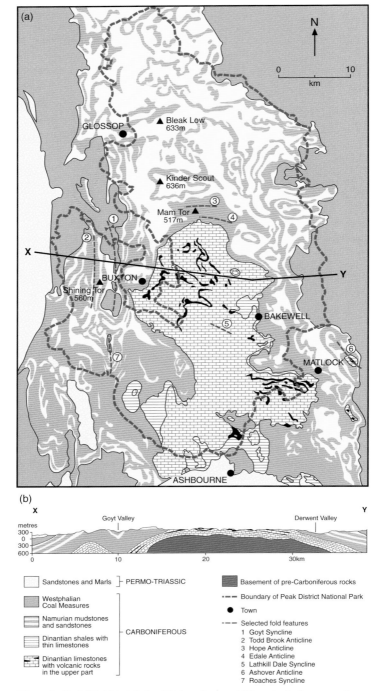

Figure 2: Peak District: (a) simplified geology and (b) geological cross-section.

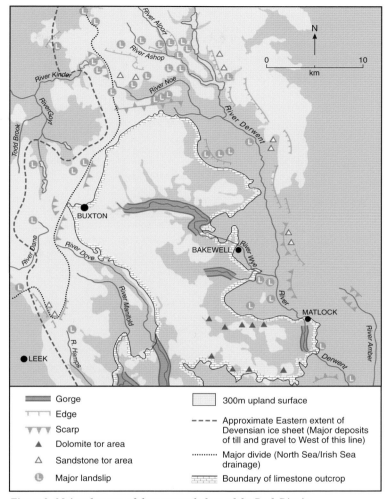

Figure 3: Major elements of the geomorphology of the Peak District.

valley sides and hill slopes incorporate competent sandstones overlying impermeable shales. Landslips are likely to occur in such circumstances and are exemplified by Mam Tor and other sites in the Vale of Edale.

In the broad structural sense the western and eastern margins of the Peak District are coincident with the western and eastern limbs of the Derbyshire Dome, or regional anticlinal structure. However, both margins exhibit clear examples of the relationships which can exist between smaller-scale fold structures and surface form. On the western margin is a series of sharply developed and broadly parallel **anticlines** and **synclines.** The Goyt and Roaches synclines have been selected for detailed discussion. On the eastern margin the Namurian strata dip eastwards at shallow angles but this regional character is

Table 1: Major stages in the development of the
Peak District landscape

Stage (climate)	Approximate date (years BP)	Geomorphological activity
Flandrian or Holocene (postglacial) *Temperate*		Re-establishment of interglacial stream pattern; formation of modern floodplains, development of soil and vegetation cover, variously reactivation of landslips and stabilisation of slopes; formation of peat.
	10,000	
Late Pleistocene Devensian (last glacial) *Cold (with short warm phases)*		Periglacial degradation, freeze-thaw weathering, scree formation, tor formation, landslips, solifluction, deposition of sheets of head; smoothing out of irregularities, levelling of interfluves; valley incision by seasonal streams. Direct glaciation of western margins, deposition of till, formation of meltwater channels.
Ipswichian (last interglacial) *Temperate*	110,000	Dissection of glacial deposits on interfluves, fluvial aggradation in main valleys, deep weathering of bedrock.
Middle Pleistocene *Alternations of cold and temperate episodes*	130,000	During cold stages: glacial erosion of bedrock and older drift deposits; deposition of till over an irregular land surface; widespread drainage modification initiating present-day drainage pattern. During temperate stages: formation of deeply weathered regoliths.
Early Pleistocene *General cooling but with climatic fluctuations*	700,000	Continued uplift; erosion of pre-Pleistocene landscape; valley incision.
	1,800,000	
Late Tertiary or Neogene		Emergence of upland Britain and initiation of streams; exposure of Carboniferous bedrock; deposition of sediments over a former land surface some 150m above present ground level; progressive uplift of Peak District.
	25,000,000	

disrupted by anticlinal structures which are located south and east of
Matlock. In consequence the overall west to east extent of the outcrop
is increased and the Dinantian limestone is brought to the surface as
the core of anticlinal folds at Crich and Ashover.

In contrast, at the northern margins in the vicinity of Castleton, the
Dinantian limestone plunges beneath the sequence of Namurian
strata. In this area the folding is gentle and runs west to east,
transverse to the north to south alignment of the Derbyshire Dome.
Many of the outcrops in this area, as on the margins of the Kinder
Scout Plateau, indicate horizontal or near horizontal strata.

The most recent and probably the most important factors in
landform development in the Dark Peak were the processes
associated with the major climatic changes of the Pleistocene. The
sequence of changes is complex (see Table 1 for summary), and it
appears that the Peak District was over-ridden by ice during the pre-

Devensian glacial episodes but only fragmentary **till** deposits remain as legacies from these events. The last glacial stage, the Devensian, saw the ice sheet reach its maximum extent about 20 000 years ago. It advanced southwards across the lowlands of Cheshire and Staffordshire and expanded into the upland margins of the Dark Peak where extensive spreads of till are the main evidence for the former presence of ice (Figure 3). However, much of the Peak was ice free and consequently subjected to an extended period of periglacial conditions. Spectacular features fashioned and modified under periglaciation are the ubiquitous edges and tors associated with the various scarps developed on the sandstones and gritstones (Figure 3). During the post-glacial Holocene widespread slope instability occurred in the form of landslides – of which nearly 600 have been identified in the Dark Peak. On the upland surfaces peat formed extensively and has been subject to severe erosion in the recent historical period. The latter is but one aspect of major human impacts on the landscape which include deforestation of the uplands, extensive quarrying of the sandstone outcrops and the flooding of deeper valleys for water storage.

The localities which are described in this book are a small but representative selection and the reader must bear in mind that many similar features can be found throughout the Dark Peak.

THE
WESTERN MARGINS

The western margin of the Dark Peak exhibits three major characteristics, which are revealed in part by its elevation in relation to adjacent areas. From the vicinity of Whaley Bridge in the north it extends some 25km south towards Leek, while its width from west to east between Macclesfield and Buxton is 10km (Figure 1). To the west the fault-guided boundary with the Cheshire Plain is well defined while to the east the geological contrast and the lower elevation of the Dinantian limestone of the White Peak are clearly evident. To the north the open valleys of the River Goyt and its tributaries give rise to topographic breaks between the western margins and the Kinder Scout Plateau. To the south, in the area around Leek, the Namurian rocks give way to the Westphalian of the Potteries region (Figure 2).

Dissected plateau form

The area comprises a dissected plateau which reaches elevations in excess of 450m **OD**, the highest being Shining Tor (SJ 995737) at 559m. The degree and pattern of dissection are quite marked. The majority of the rivers of the area, principally the Goyt and the Dane, drain westwards to the Cheshire Plain and eventually reach the Irish Sea via the Mersey. Only in the southern extremity do the headwaters of the River Churnet form a component of the Trent system. In this locality the area between the Churnet and the Dane is the main watershed of England demarcating Irish Sea orientated drainage from North Sea drainage. This watershed, as it runs northwards to the Kinder Scout Plateau, broadly coincides with the eastern boundary of the western margins.

Geological control

Within the western margins geological control of landform is fundamental. Indeed there are few elements of the relief which do not exhibit such control. There are two facets of the geological scene which are important. First, the successions of weak shales and resistant sandstones and second the influence of anticlinal, synclinal and fault structures. The most significant of these are aligned north to south and comprise sub-parallel folds and faults. The particular combination of lithology and structure is strongly reflected in the pattern of relief and drainage. Yet, despite evidence of structural control of many elements of the physical landscape, such as the anticlinal Todd Brook valley and the synclinal Goyt Valley, the overall drainage pattern is discordant. This implies that superimposition followed by partial readjustment has been the essential course of events. It is unclear, from the evidence available, whether superimposition took place from a cover of Mesozoic rocks which once extended across the entire area of the Peak, or from a cover of Tertiary rocks. Additionally, events in the Pleistocene may have given rise to conditions where drainage patterns were significantly altered.

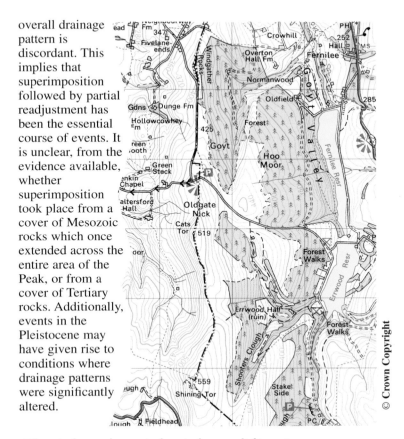

© Crown Copyright

Glacial and periglacial modification

The western margins of the Dark Peak were strongly influenced by glacial and periglacial processes. The most recent phase of activity occurred in the late Devensian when an ice sheet advanced southwards across the Cheshire Plain and impinged on the hill margins to the west (Figure 3). The distribution of superficial deposits as mapped by the British Geological Survey shows an abundance of till and glacial sands and gravels on the western side adjacent to the Cheshire Plain. In contrast the eastern side is dominated by **head** deposits indicative of the intensity of past periglacial conditions. This distribution suggests that the penetration of the ice into the western margins was limited, the advance seemingly being greatest up the major valleys such as the Goyt into the basin around Chapel-en-le-Frith and Hayfield. Possible ice-related features within the area are systems of channels which are anomalous in relation to the present drainage. These have been variously interpreted as cut by ice-marginal or sub-glacial **meltwaters.**

THE GOYT VALLEY

The upper Goyt Valley is a synclinally guided trough which extends approximately 14km along a north-to-south axis between New Mills (SK 002855) and Derbyshire Bridge (SK 017718). The main valley receives a number of tributaries, the principal being Todd Brook which runs parallel to the River Goyt to the west and is structurally guided by a faulted anticline. Structural control of the landform at the wider scale is best observed in the vicinity of the Fernilee and Errwood reservoirs (Figure 4). The vantage point at SK 018772 is recommended for a general view of this area. The extent of modification of the valley floor by reservoir construction is clearly evident and at times of low water the depth of incision of the former river course can be appreciated.

In this locality two Namurian sandstone formations, Chatsworth Grit and Rough Rock, 40m and 30m thick respectively, are the main scarp-forming beds. These are separated by some 30m of shales. Westphalian strata, which succeed the Namurian, are preserved at the centre of the Goyt Syncline north of Fernilee Reservoir and also occur to the east as a result of faulting. Within the Westphalian, the Woodhead Sandstone tends to form strong scarp features comparable to those associated with the Chatsworth Grit and Rough Rock (Figure 4a). Dip values are variable on both limbs of the Goyt Syncline and increase from about 14° at the outer margins to 45° towards the axis of the fold. In the vicinity of Fernilee and Errwood reservoirs the alignment of the Goyt Valley and the axis of the syncline coincide closely. On the western flanks of the valley minor tributary streams have responded to the sequence of weak shales and resistant grits to produce scarp and vale topography. The upper reaches of the Mill Clough and Shooter's Clough streams flow along the **strike** of the beds on the shales and have eroded down-dip to produce west-facing scarps on the Rough Rock outcrop. Tors, free faces and **blockfields** are features of these scarps, notably at Foxlow Edge (SK 005753). Head deposits are widespread throughout the area. From the scarp crests, extensive, evenly graded slopes incline eastwards towards the centre of the Goyt trough at angles of between 8° and 14°, which approximate to the angle of dip of the Rough Rock.

Immediately west of the Rough Rock scarp, the Chatsworth Grit forms a parallel feature. The crest of this scarp takes the form of a prominent ridge extending due north from Shining Tor (SJ 995737), 559m, over a distance of 5km to Windgather Rocks (SJ 995783), 430m. Along this scarp face is a series of tor and edge features at Shining Tor, Cats Tor (SJ 995759), Oldgate Nick (SJ 996763), Pym

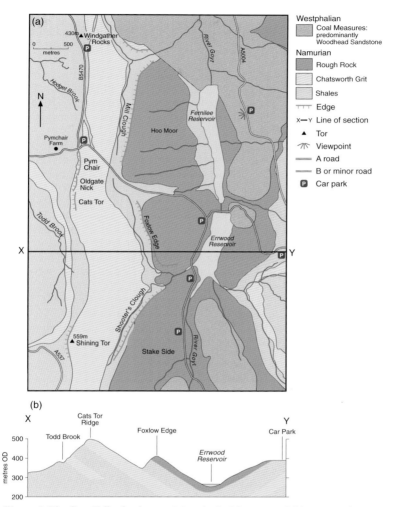

Figure 4: The Goyt Valley landscape: (a) geological features and (b) cross-section.

Chair (SJ 996766) and Windgather Rocks. The free faces of these edges are 15m to 25m high but have been modified by quarrying. The eastward dip of the strata is evident in all cases particularly where mushroom-like tor features occur, as at Windgather Rocks. To the east of the scarp crest the slopes developed on the Chatsworth Grit descend into the upper strike-guided reaches of the Mill and Shooter's Clough valleys and carry an extensive cover of upland peat deposits.

The view westward from the Chatsworth Grit scarp crest is dominated by Todd Brook Valley. The relief of the valley is complex, reflecting structural, glacial and fluvial influences in detail, but in broad terms representing an excellent example of a breached anticline. The exploitation of the anticline by Todd Brook has been aided by a well developed fault which runs the length of the flexure. The Chatsworth Grit scarp forms the eastern limb of the anticline.

Access

To examine the landforms of the Goyt area in detail an excursion on foot is advised. This will take a whole day and although the walking is relatively easy, appropriate outdoor clothing (particularly waterproof footwear) will be needed as the peaty ground can be extremely wet underfoot.

The car park by Errwood Reservoir (SK 012748) (which is not suitable for coaches and not accessible from Derbyshire Bridge) is a good starting point. The path which leads south-westwards from the car park traverses the Rough Rock outcrop and leads to the edge above Shooter's Clough. From here views of the strike valleys and Foxlow Edge can be gained. By following the path to the head of Shooter's Clough the scarp crest of the Chatsworth Grit is reached at Shining Tor. This can then be followed northwards and the various edge, tor and blockfield features explored *en route*. The breached anticline of the Todd Brook can also be viewed to the west. At Windgather Rocks follow paths eastwards into the Goyt trough and return to the car park via the west side of Fernilee Reservoir. For a shorter journey, the car parks at Pym Chair (SJ 996767) and Windgather Rocks (SJ 995782) give easier access to the Chatsworth Grit scarp on the west side of the Goyt Valley.

THE ROACHES

The Goyt Syncline continues southwards to the vicinity of Leek where the fold closes. Its association with landform is particularly significant in the region of The Roaches (SK 003627) and the neighbouring Ramshaw Rocks (SK 020626) (Figure 5 and Photo 1). In general the relationship between geology and landform is similar to that described in the Goyt Valley, in that the effects of the sequence of resistant grits and weak shales is clearly exemplified. However, there are important contrasts which arise from the plunging form of the syncline in this locality and also the discordant nature of the drainage pattern.

The effect of differential erosion of the strata is apparent on both limbs of the Roaches Syncline. On the south-west side of the structure three resistant grit formations form marked scarp features, namely the Five Clouds Sandstone, the Roaches Grit and the Chatsworth Grit. These combine to form a spectacular stepped scarp. The lower formation, the Five Clouds Sandstone, comprises some 100m of sandstones which produces a prominent edge some 25m in height over a horizontal distance of 1km. A narrow but clearly developed structural bench associated with the top of the Five Clouds Sandstone then gives way to an even more prominent scarp. This coincides with

Photo 1: The Roaches Syncline viewed from the south, Hen Cloud to the left, Ramshaw Rocks to the right. Photo: Roger Dalton.

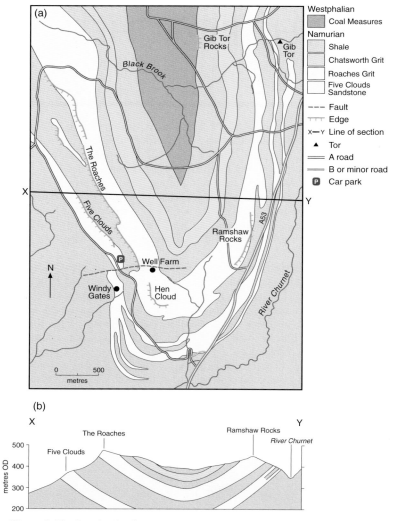

Figure 5: The Roaches landscape: *(a) geological features and (b) cross-section.*

the Roaches Grit and, reaching a height of 35m, extends over 2km between points at grid references SJ 995645 and SK 006622. Although widespread quarrying has modified the edge features below the scarp crest, the crest itself consists of highly weathered sandstone. Rounded boulders and groups of blocks forming tors and pinnacle features are common. Contrasts between thinly bedded and massively bedded sandstones, the effects of the exploitation of vertical jointing and the differential weathering of cross bedding in the sandstone can be observed in many places. The relatively high dip values of over 20° can be seen in the attitude of the rock formations.

Collectively the surface forms represent a spectacular example of a landscape fashioned under periglacial conditions. The accumulations of weathered debris both at the foot of the edge features and on the surface of the back slope of the Roaches Grit include many detached blocks which are truly massive (see Figure 11 for an illustration of tor formation, page 43). The effectiveness of the downslope rafting of material under freeze-thaw conditions is clearly demonstrated. To the south of The Roaches the Five Clouds Sandstone and Roaches Grit terminate abruptly at a fault-guided depression at SK 007620, between Windygates and Well Farm (Figure 5a). Beyond is the hill feature known as Hen Cloud (SK 008615) which has a similar geological structure to The Roaches and, when viewed in profile (Photo 2), reveals a classic scarp and dip (backslope) form fringed extensively with weathered debris.

On the opposite eastern limb of the Goyt Syncline the dominant landscape feature is an east-facing scarp known as Ramshaw Rocks (SK 020626) which extends 1km from north to south. The scarp again represents the strong topographic expression of the Roaches Grit and displays similar features to The Roaches itself. The Five Clouds Sandstone also outcrops on the valley side below Ramshaw Rocks but here this formation is sub-divided into a sequence of sandstone beds separated by shales, and minor bench features only are present.

Towards the centre of the Roaches Syncline the Chatsworth Grit produces minor edge features. These may be seen at Gib Tor Rocks (SK 018648) and at other localities such as SK 010623. As in the Goyt Valley the lower Westphalian strata form a central outlier. There is, however, a contrast in the pattern of drainage in that the streams do not follow the axial alignment of the fold. The greater part of the drainage is orientated north-westwards, to Black Brook, a tributary of

Photo 2: Hen Cloud in profile. *Photo: Roger Dalton.*

the River Dane. Black Brook follows a discordant route across the Roaches Syncline and leaves by way of a valley developed along the strike of the shale beds between the Roaches and Chatsworth Grits. The grits form a prominent edge with fringing blockfield in the vicinity of Cloughhead (SK 002651). There is, however, a broad vale leading northwards between Sniddles Head Farm (SK 005653) and Little Hillend (SK 013654) through which drainage might have achieved a more structurally sympathetic route to the Upper Dane.

A further discordant element in the drainage pattern occurs in the vicinity of Upper Hulme (SK 011610). Here a deeply cut valley is occupied by a stream whose headwaters drain the southernmost part of the synclinal depression. The Roaches Grit scarp is thus effectively breached.

Explanations of drainage discordancy are various and difficult to substantiate. One possibility involves the influence of the Devensian ice sheet. During the period of its maximum extent the ice limit is believed to have been in the vicinity of The Roaches. The ice could have abutted against or even over-ridden the scarp. Early workers on this problem, such as Jowett and Charlesworth in 1929, argued for the existence of an ice-dammed lake which was trapped in the synclinal basin of The Roaches. The present course of Black Brook and its headwaters then developed after the lacustrine stage while the valley leading through Upper Hulme (SK 011610) could have been cut as the lake waters overspilled the line of the scarp. However, explanations involving temporary glacially-impounded lakes are no longer widely accepted in the absence of unequivocal supporting evidence such as the occurrence of proven lake-floor sediments.

An alternative explanation for drainage discordance at ice margins involves sub-glacial meltwater erosion. Channels may have been eroded as the ice began to melt and, once formed, they were incorporated into the drainage pattern that is evident today. Implicit support for such a hypothesis is provided by the presence of a feature which has the characteristic form of meltwater channels on the opposite side of the upper Churnet valley less than 1km distant from Upper Hulme. This channel with steep sides and flat floor begins at Blackshawmoor Reservoir (SK 017599) and is traceable 6km southward along the outer margin of the Dark Peak to the head of Combes Valley (SK 023535). The floor of the channel at Blackshawmoor is about 290m which is an indicator that the ice margin must have reached at least this level, perhaps throughout the area of The Roaches. A consequence would be that ice could have penetrated the Roaches Syncline along the line of the upper Hulme valley and possibly the Well Farm depression (SK 007621) which stands at 340m. Further to the north, ice could have penetrated the Black Brook valley below Cloughhead.

A further possibility is that river capture has taken place. The Black Brook can be envisaged as working headwards along the strike of the weaker shales into the synclinal basin. The Upper Hulme stream could similarly have encroached into the scarp face perhaps by a process of headward sapping by springs.

The highest points on The Roaches, Hen Cloud and Ramshaw Rocks are all excellent vantage points from which the broad characteristic of the landforms of the Roaches Syncline can be observed. In addition there are views across the less elevated landscape to the south and west. This tract of country has the form of a broad vale and also illustrates the importance of ice sheets in shaping landforms. The vale is floored by glacial till which often has a distinctive **drumlinoid** form, apparent in the area to the north-west of Tittesworth Reservoir (SJ 990600).

Access

The Roaches area is best approached from the A53 between Leek and Buxton. The narrow minor roads with occasional steep gradients are only suitable for cars and minibuses. The Roaches scarp can be reached easily from the restricted roadside parking at SK 003622. As the area is much used by climbers, space may be limited, especially at weekends. Other restricted roadside parking is available at SJ 996645 at the north-west end of The Roaches ridge, and at SK 018619 near to Ramshaw Rocks.

THE NORTHERN MARGINS

Photo 3: Kinder Downfall. *Photo: Roger Dalton.*

The northern margins of the Dark Peak incorporate a range of contrasting relief elements. The essential characteristic is that of an extensive elevated plateau which is deeply dissected. Kinder Scout, reaching 636m, is one facet of the plateau and is the most elevated tract of country in the Dark Peak. The drainage pattern of the area is broadly **dendritic** with a strong easterly component which reflects structural control. On the northern edge of the White Peak the Dinantian limestones plunge beneath the Namurian sandstones so that the Derbyshire Dome gives way to an area where sub-parallel west to east trending structures are dominant (see also Dalton *et al.*, 1999). These flexures are gentle relative to those of the River Goyt and Todd Brook valleys, but are still significant. The Hope and Edale valleys are broadly coincident with anticlines while the Kinder Scout area corresponds to a shallow syncline.

Throughout the area slopes are relatively steep and exhibit good examples of landslips and periglacial slope phenomena. Landslips are particularly numerous (Figure 6) and although the features of Edale and Mam Tor are relatively easy to access, other valuable visits are feasible for those equipped to explore more remote localities. These include the scarp face below Kinder Downfall (SK 082887) (Photo 3), Alport Castles (SK 142913), Seal Edge (SK 105887) (Photo 4) and Seal Stones (SK 112888) where possible incipient corrie features have been identified.

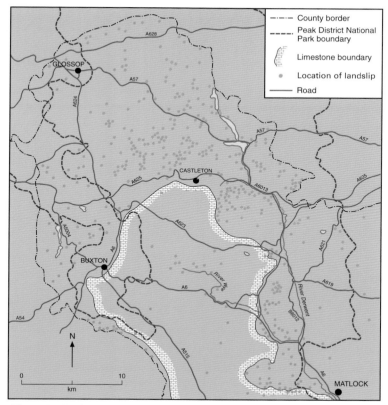

Figure 6: Distribution of landslips in north-west Derbyshire.
After: Doornkamp, 1990.

Photo 4: Seal Edge showing free face and blockfield. *Photo: Roger Dalton.*

EDALE AND KINDER SCOUT

Photo 5: Edale Head from Kinder Low. *Photo: Roger Dalton.*

The Vale of Edale is a visually attractive valley, drained by the River Noe. It extends some 8km from Edale Head (SK 085870) in the west to Edale End (SK 162863) in the east, at which point the River Noe effects a narrow exit before turning to flow southwards. In its broader western and central parts the width of the valley is 5km. The overall form of the relief and drainage of Edale is asymmetrical with the River Noe flowing closest to its southern watershed. To the north and west the sides of the Vale of Edale reach elevations of 530-630m OD (Photo 5) and form the margins of the extensive plateaus of Kinder Scout and Edale Moor. These have been deeply dissected by the upper Noe and its major north bank tributaries Crowden Brook, Grinds Brook, Oller Brook and Lady Booth Brook. To the south Edale is divided from the Hope Valley by a narrow ridge which reaches 400-500m OD. From this ridge the River Noe receives numerous, closely spaced minor tributaries. On the floor of the Vale courses of the River Noe and its tributaries are incised up to 15m and display a variety of fluvial forms including a well developed sequence of terraces.

Bedrock lithology and structure have a fundamental influence on the gross morphology of the Vale of Edale. The essential feature is the alternation of weak shales, dominant across the floor of the Vale, and

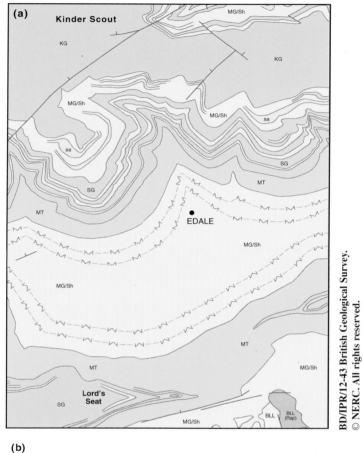

BD/IPR/12-43 British Geological Survey.
© NERC. All rights reserved.

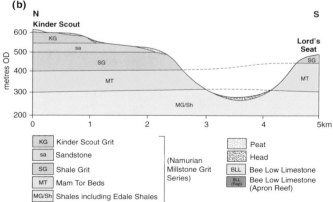

		(Namurian Millstone Grit Series)
KG	Kinder Scout Grit	
sa	Sandstone	
SG	Shale Grit	
MT	Mam Tor Beds	
MG/Sh	Shales including Edale Shales	

	Peat
	Head
BLL	Bee Low Limestone
BLL (Rap)	Bee Low Limestone (Apron Reef)

Figure 7: Vale of Edale: (a) bedrock geology, and (b) north to south cross-section.
Reproduced by permission of the Director, British Geological Survey. © NERC.
All rights reserved.

stronger sandstones prominent on the upper slopes. On the north side the Kinder Scout Grit provides a highly resistant capping to the summit areas, while the Shale Grit coincides with distinctive bench features on the spurs between the dissecting valleys. The Kinder Scout Grit has been removed from the less elevated southern side so that the Mam Tor Sandstones and outliers of Shale Grit cap the ridge (Figure 7). Although fold structures are not strongly developed, Edale does relate to a shallow anticline with a west to east axis broadly coincident with the course of the River Noe.

A significant factor in the development of Edale's present landscape was the prolonged episode of periglacial conditions during the late Pleistocene (Table 1, page 10). This gave rise to a range of depositional environments, which have left their mark on the form of the land surface within the Vale of Edale mainly as a result of the accumulation of periglacial slope deposits (head), peat and landslip material (Figure 7).

Periglacial slope deposits or head as mapped by the Geological Survey are depicted as completely filling the floor and lower slopes of Edale and tonguing up the valleys of the major tributaries of the River Noe. In terms of its extent, head is a highly significant element in the Edale scene. Its presence is not immediately obvious because of late post-glacial weathering and **slopewash.** Agricultural activities such as ploughing and stone picking have also served to smooth out irregularities in the ground surface. Close inspection reveals that the Vale floor is slightly undulating, and in the vicinity of some tributary valleys, e.g. Grinds Brook (SK 115873), the head occurs as fan-like masses.

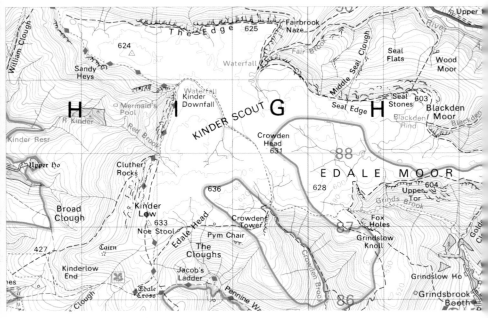

© **Crown Copyright**

Head is an accumulation of poorly sorted debris from the disintegration and downslope movement of local bedrock material. Such downslope movement accelerated during periglacial episodes which reduced the strength of the bedrock and facilitated frost creep and solifluction through the alternation of freezing and thawing. Minimal vegetation cover allowed material to move unimpeded so the head developed by the downslope movement and cumulative accretion of what was, in effect, a semi-fluid substance. Accumulations of head up to 10m thick have been noted in the Vale of Edale (Figure 7) and two stream bank exposures were described by Wilson in 1981, an example of which is seen in the Ashop Valley north of Edale (Photo 6). At Grindsbrook Booth (SK 123860) the source materials are derived from upslope areas on the north side of the Vale which provide a predominance of large-calibre sandstone clasts to the head matrix. Whereas at Barber Booth (SK 113847) the source material is from the southern flank, where a greater occurrence of shale bedrock makes for a finer matrix. Other exposures of head occur in stream banks, for example to the west and east of Lee Farm (SK 097855) where ochrous head can be clearly distinguished from the underlying grey/purple Edale shales.

Head also occurs on the upper slopes on the northern side of Edale, particularly on the structural benches coincident with the Shale Grit. The landscape above the benches has much in common with the grit edges of Hathersage Moor. Slopes are frequently strewn with large boulders, rafted under freeze-thaw activity and stranded as slope angles decreased or climatic conditions ameliorated. The sources of the boulders are gritstone edges, some of which have a typical tor

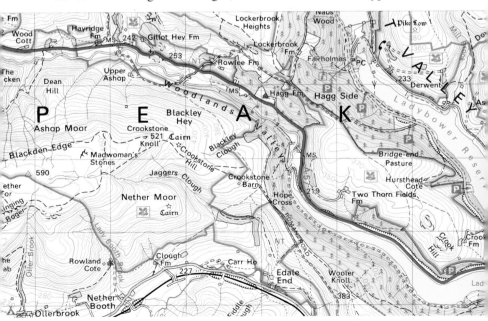

form, as at Noe Stool (SK 082869) and Crowden Tower (SK 094871). In the same areas are numerous weirdly-shaped smaller tors which have been smoothed and rounded by post-glacial weathering and erosion (Photo 7a).

Photo 6: Ashop Valley. *Head deposit overlying convoluted outcrop of Edale Shales. Photo: Howard Fox.*

The footpath between the top of Grinds Brook (SK 105873) and Edale Cross (SK 077861) provides many opportunities to observe tors and associated features. It also skirts the margins of the blanket peat landscape of the Kinder Scout plateau to the north of Edale (Photo 7a). The lower edge of the peat is at about 500m OD and is conspicuous through the change in vegetation type, with which it coincides (Photo 7). The peat reaches a thickness of 3m and post-dates the formation of Crowden Tower and the other tors that emerge through the peat cover. Pollen analysis has shown that sphagnum peat grew between 8000 and 6500 years **BP** when its development was favoured by climatic conditions that were warmer and wetter than those of today. The formation of the peat may also have been facilitated by burning and grazing during the Mesolithic which checked colonisation of upland areas by woody plants. The contemporary peat landscape is made more distinctive by the extent to which it has been eroded (Photo 8). This may have begun as early as 1000 years BP through bog bursts and slides at the margins of the peat masses which initiated gulleying which has progressively extended back into the peat. Meandering stream patterns have cut through the peat to reveal gritstone bedrock and associated weathered material. The vegetation cover has been removed over wide areas such that about 8% of the uplands are now bare peat. The exposed peat surfaces are treacherously sticky in wet weather and liable to wind erosion when they dry out. It is likely that digging, grazing, burning, drainage cuts and walkers have in their various ways

(a)

Photo 7: Kinder Scout Plateau:
(a) the level of the path shows the
depth to which peat has been eroded,
and (b) a peat profile.
Photos: Roger Dalton.

(b)

initiated and sustained erosion. However, it is now thought that airborne pollution from adjacent industrial areas has adversely affected the peat because plants, like sphagnum, which are fundamental to the form-ation of peat are particularly sensitive to sulphur dioxide. This accords with the view that peat erosion has been especially active since the early nineteenth century.

Slope instability is widespread in the Vale of Edale and evident at a variety of scales (Photo 9) ranging from the ubiquitous hill slope terracettes and turf slumpings to major landslips. The larger slips are comparable to that at Mam Tor (see page 34).

Three local features combine to create situations in which slopes are inherently unstable. These are the rock succession where resistant sandstones overlie less competent shales, erosional regimes which have fashioned steep slopes, and the weakening of slopes through deep penetration by frost under periglacial conditions. It is not easy to explain why a slope should fail in one place and not in others. In the Vale of Edale water would appear to play a significant role in view of the numerous seepages at spring heads at the sandstone/shale boundary (Figure 8). In some instances of landslipping, heavy rainfall may have initiated failure of the shales through increased **pore water**

Photo 8: Severe peat erosion on Kinder Scout. Photo: Roger Dalton.

pressure and consequent reduction in shear strength. However, another cause of slope failure might be oversteepening by lateral stream erosion at the slope foot. Such events must have occurred in recent geological time because some Edale landslips overlie head deposits.

The dating of Edale landslips is problematic. Peat incorporated in the landslips at Edale End below Lose Hill (SK 155854) has been dated to between 3500 and 2500 years BP, but peat associated with slips in Alport Valley (SK 138910) to the north has been dated at around 8000 years BP (Johnson and Vaughan, 1983).

Most of the Edale landslips relate to the boundary between the Mam Tor Beds and Edale Shales. South-east of Edale Head House (SK 087860) a relatively simple slip occurs which comprises a single slumped mass with a flow of what was well lubricated material in the toe area. Larger slips with well marked slip scars are located at Edale End (SK 162862), where lateral erosion by the River Noe has caused undercutting. While such activity has sustained instability, so that movement has taken place progressively over a period, it is not clear whether this triggered the original failure. At the Broadlee-bank Tor slip (SK 110857) (Photo 10) the Mam Tor beds are well exposed in the slip scar and the irregular topography of the slumped mass, covering 10ha, can be explored from a public footpath at the foot of the slip.

Cracks in the turf suggest that movement is still taking place. The larger landslide at Back Tor (SK 146852), which has an area of 60ha, is essentially similar with the slip scar forming a prominent land mark on the southern rim of Edale. In both cases the slips comprise a

Photo 9: An extensive area of land slipping on the southern side of the Vale of Edale. Photo: Roger Dalton.

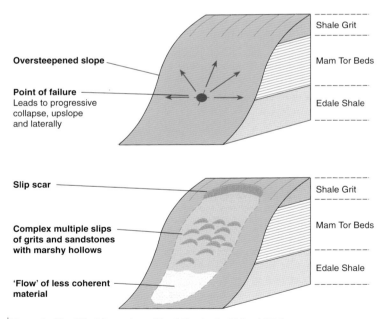

Figure 8: Simplified formation of landslips in the Vale of Edale.

complex of rotational forms which have created enclosed hollows marked by marshy ground. Large slips also occur at Greenlands (SK 128845) and to the north-west of Mam Tor (SK 128840). These slips are best appreciated from the footpaths skirting their upper margins, from which the irregular surfaces of the slipped material can be seen

Photo 10: Broadlee-bank landslip on the northern side of the Vale of Edale.
Photo: Roger Dalton.

to incorporate numerous marshy hollows with some open pools of water.

Other slips occur on the northern side of Edale where shales have failed beneath the Kinder Scout Grit as in the valleys at upper Grinds Brook, Golden Clough and Jaggers Clough (SK 119874, 121873, 145879). Large fallen blocks of sandstone lie downslope of the slip scars forming areas of highly broken ground.

Access and safety
The Vale of Edale is deservedly a very popular area with walkers, the village of Edale being located at the southern end of the Pennine Way. The landforms described are all accessible from public footpaths. The network of paths is good and well marked, and visitors are urged not to stray from them and to respect the farming activities of the Vale. The areas of greatest danger are Kinder Scout Plateau and Edale Moor. The peat surface is difficult for walking and direction finding and in poor visibility demands the use of a compass.

Road access to Edale is the A625 between Chapel-en-le-Frith and Sheffield, turning off at SK 122832 or Hope village centre (SK 172835). Coaches must use the Hope village access route and park in the pay-and-display car park south of Edale village (SK 124853). This is also the best place to park cars though other car parks/picnic areas are at Upper Booth (SK 104854) and south-west of Mam Tor (SK 124832). Rail services between Manchester and Sheffield stop at Edale station (SK 122853).

MAM TOR

L ying at the head of the Hope Valley and on its northern slope, the sheer eastern face of Mam Tor forms a conspicuous landmark. This face represents the back scar of one of the best known landslide complexes in the Peak District. The scar itself is some 65m in height and the displaced mass of debris covers an area of approximately 35ha (Figure 9a). The whole landslide has been described as a complex rotational slump. Movement in the upper part of the slide consists of rotational slipping on a concave failure surface, as attested by the dip of the shales in the slide units. This approaches 55° due to the back tilting, compared with a gentle 5° dip to the north-east on *in situ* bedrock on the main scarp face. Initial failure must have involved rapid movement since highly polished rock surfaces have been detected just below the scar. In the toe region, translational sliding and earthflows have also occurred and can be seen clearly when the slumped mass is viewed from surrounding high points.

Much of the geological setting of the landslip is revealed by the back scar which exposes thinly bedded Namurian sandstones, known as the Mam Tor Beds. These are underlain by black pyritic shales, the Edale Shales, which are poorly exposed. The Namurian sequence lies unconformably upon the Carboniferous (Dinantian) limestones (Figure 9b) which outcrop a few metres to the south. It is the alternation of sandstones and shales of different strength which in part provides the environment of instability. In addition, a major fault runs through the southern side of the main scar face from the west and provides an outlet for water seepage.

Water is known to play an important role in the generation of landsliding, largely through the production of high pore pressures. In the case of Mam Tor the role of water as an agent of decomposition may be linked with chemical factors. The toe region of the slipped material is characterised by the emergence of red-stained, sulphate-rich, acidic waters typical of pyrite oxidation. However, a recent study has shown that most of the sulphuric acid generated by oxidation is consumed by clay mineral alteration and carbonate dissolution. Such reactions cause a weakening of the rock structure and hence may contribute to slope instability.

At present the slipped mass is affected by relatively frequent small movements with major movements occurring only intermittently. The small failures may be triggered by increased pore pressures after periods of high rainfall whilst major movements may be preceded by chemical decomposition along the slip zone. With stability reduced to a low level other factors may then trigger failure. A rise in

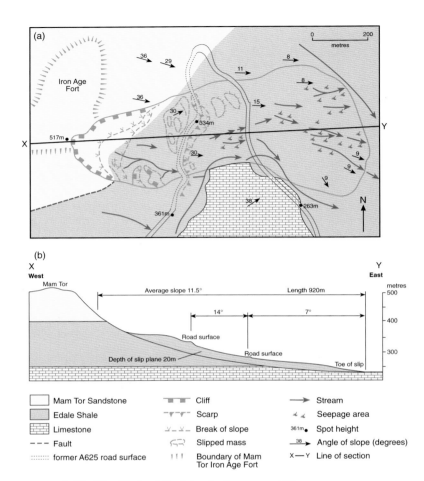

Figure 9: The Mam Tor landslip: (a) major features, and (b) west to east cross-section.

groundwater level, loading of the main unit by debris falling from the back scar or removal of support from the toe by small-scale movements may all be responsible.

Repeated movement of the landslip (which has earned Mam Tor the nickname of 'the shivering mountain') necessitated the continual repair and eventual closure, in 1979, of the A625 Sheffield to Manchester road (Figure 9a). The destruction of the road surface provides a spectacular example of the nature and impact of landsliding (Photo 11). Evidence of the attempts to keep the road open by continual resurfacing and minor engineering works is clearly visible. Movement of the landslide continues and recent measurements show rates of movement of 104mm per month.

The dating of the main rotational landslips is difficult. It is not clear whether the Iron Age fort on the summit of Mam Tor was constructed

Photo 11: Deformation of the road surface on Mam Tor. *Photo: Peter Jones.*

before or after the main failure since there is no conclusive evidence that the ditch and bank were ever complete. Dates obtained from other landslips in the area suggest that **mass movement** has been active from the late Devensian to the present day. No major movements are taking place in the main back scar area at the present time but weathering produces considerable rock fall activity.

Access

Mam Tor can be approached along the A625 which is closed in the vicinity of the landslip. Cars and minibuses can traverse Winnats Pass to the south, but, as the Pass is steep and winding, coaches are prohibited. Car parks are located to the west of Mam Tor on the A625 (at SK 124832) and to the east (at SK 141828). Coach and car parks are to be found at the west end of Castleton village (SK 149830).

The base of the back scar must be approached with care as rockfall commonly occurs. A flagged footpath runs up the western flank of the scar to the summit of Mam Tor and continues along the crest of the ridge via Hollins Cross (SK 136845) to Lose Hill (SK 155854) giving fine views of Edale and Hope Valley. From Hollins Cross a south-west descent allows the opportunity to investigate the landslipped road.

THE
EASTERN MARGINS

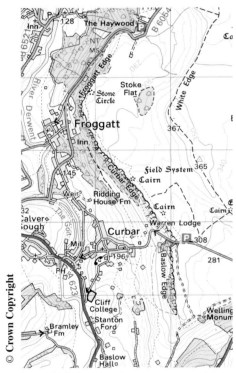

© Crown Copyright

Located to the east of the River Derwent, the eastern margins of the Dark Peak are narrower and structurally less complex than the western margins. The Derwent is the main river of the Peak District and flows southwards in a **superimposed** fashion so that it transgresses the boundary between the Namurian and Dinantian outcrops. Structurally the area is divisible into two sections.

From the northern Hallam Moors (SK 240860) west of Sheffield 18km southwards to Beeley Moor (SK 290675) the Namurian rocks dip eastwards at shallow angles of 2° or 3°. The main relief feature is a **cuesta** with well developed scarp and backslope features. The scarps are frequently exaggerated by edge features while the backslopes extend some 4km from west to east before giving way to the overlying Westphalian outcrop.

To the south and east of Beeley Moor the Namurian outcrop widens as a result of the presence of minor fold structures. These are most prominent when developed as anticlinal flexures as at Crich and Ashover. The Ashover Anticline, traversed longitudinally by the River Amber, provides a classic example of the inversion of relief similar to Todd Brook Valley and making an interesting comparison with the western synclinal forms of the Goyt Valley and The Roaches.

The areas studied in the following three sections: The Derwent edges, Tors in the Hathersage area and the Ashover Anticline, provide examples of the diversity of features on the eastern margins of the Peak District.

THE
DERWENT EDGES

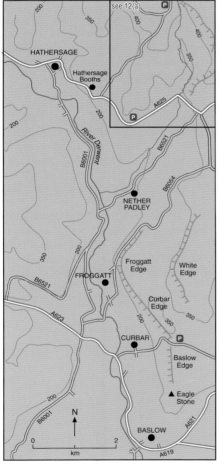

A road (========)
B or minor road (======)
Contour (m) (———)
Sandstone edge (⊤⊤⊤)
Tor (▲)
Car park (🅿)

Figure 10: The Derwent Valley: central section.

The landscape of the eastern margins of the Peak District is dominated by gritstone edges. They are particularly well developed in the upper Derwent Valley where they form a series of escarpments for 16km from Derwent Edge near Ladybower in the north (SK 195890) (see cover) to Baslow Edge in the south (SK 260740). One of the finest sections, overlooking the villages of Froggatt, Curbar and Baslow, is broken only by Curbar Gap in the south (Figure 10). The edges also form one of the major areas of tors in the Pennines.

The presence of these edges reflects the incision of major drainage lines into the broad geological structure of the Peak District. The Namurian sandstones and shales overlook the central limestone core and the sandstones form inward facing scarps (see Figure 3, page 8). However, this simple cuesta form is complicated by local flexures and faults. The result is a series of edges formed in a variety of resistant sandstones within the Namurian sequence. For example, Stanage

Edge (Photo 12 and frontispiece) north of Hathersage is developed in Chatsworth Grit whilst Froggatt Edge to the south is developed on Rough Rock. The highest members of the sequence tend to develop less substantial free faces, for example White Edge (SK 261765) formed to the east of Froggatt. This reflects upwards changes in bed thickness and grain size.

The form of the edges is typified by Curbar Edge (SK 255755) where a fractured and heavily weathered free face reaches heights of 10-18m above a west-facing debris-covered slope of between 15 and 20°. The free face is sub-divided into large blocks by widely spaced joints and in places is breached by areas of heavily shattered sandstone. In some locations the edge crest is surmounted by tors or detached blocks. Many joints have been widened by up to 1m or more and some are choked with weathered sandstone debris. Below the free face large fallen blocks are scattered across the slopes which temporary exposures have shown to be underlain by several metres of head. The ultimate form of the edges and lower slopes largely reflects the cold phases of the Quaternary with retreat occurring as a result of severe freeze-thaw, rockfall activity and downslope movement of material to form head (Photo 13). However, the impact of quarrying has altered the true natural form of the free face in a number of places such as just west of Curbar Gap (SK 260748) where unfinished millstones can still be seen.

At a more detailed scale some of the sub-horizontal sandstone surfaces display microtopography which has been termed crenellation. A variety of forms occur from small-scale surface pitting to well developed systems of ridges and hollows. These have an amplitude of only a few centimetres but are found in conjunction with bottle-

Photo 12: Stanage Edge – *the blockfield is clearly visible below the free face.*
Photo: Roger Dalton.

Photo 13: Curbar Edge with deep head deposit visible at the toe of the slope. Photo: Peter Jones.

shaped hollows and gutters up to 70cm deep. In addition, solution pans up to 1m across can be found on many sandstone surfaces. As with limestone, solution may be the cause of these features, but it is likely that a number of processes are involved working in combination. Any surface irregularity may hold standing water and this may stimulate chemical decay and enhance freeze-thaw action. The growth of lichens may further accelerate exploitation through the action of organic chemical weathering. On inclined surfaces water flow is important both in the deepening and lateral extension of the hollows.

This detailed rock surface relief is often found in association with a hardened layer up to 2.5cm thick. This layer usually has a higher iron content than fresh sandstone. In places where the crust has been removed the underlying sandstone is greyish in colour, soft and friable. This suggests that capillary water movement removes iron from the fresh sandstone, redepositing it in the surface crust. However, in some cases iron concentration can occur in the rock through seepage along joints and bedding planes and, if exposed, provide a crust unrelated to existing weathering conditions. It is clear that once the crust is breached the material beneath is easily weathered and removed, promoting the development of the microtopography.

Access

Stanage Edge can be accessed either from the A57 in the north, where off-road parking is available at SK 216874, from a car park (at SK 228844) near its central portion by taking the minor road east from the A6013 in Bamford, or from its southern end at a car park (SK 243830) reached by a minor road off the A625 in Hathersage. Burbage Rocks and Carl Wark can be reached from a small car park at SK 259829.

The edges between Hathersage and Baslow are most easily reached from the B6054 above Nether Padley and from the minor road (Curbar Lane) from Curbar through Curbar Gap. The car park at Curbar Gap (SK 262747) offers easy access to both Curbar and Baslow Edges. A small example of crenellation microtopography on the sandstone can be seen at a point about 80m north of Curbar Gap. A walk along the top of Curbar Edge (investigating the sandstone surfaces) will bring you onto Froggatt Edge, you can then return via a footpath at the base of Curbar Edge to gain an impression of the free face and blockfields (a round walk of approximately 6km). Alternatively, the car park at SK 257777 on the B6054 offers access to the northern end of Froggatt.

Great care must be exercised in approaching the free faces both from above and below. Behind Baslow Edge, Eagle Stone (SK 263738) is a good example of an isolated cuboid tor similar in form and position to Mother Cap.

TORS IN THE
HATHERSAGE AREA

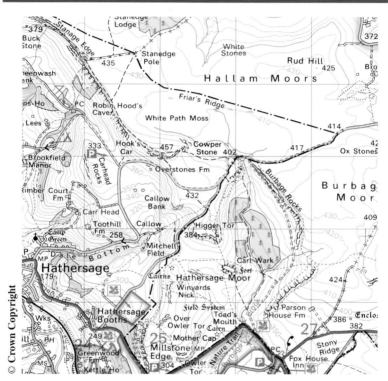

© Crown Copyright

Tors are residual, upstanding masses of bare bedrock rising from a basal rock platform which may be buried by **regolith**. They are seldom less than 3m in height or greater than 50m. Such features exist in several regions of Britain but those on Dartmoor in South West England are perhaps best known. For many years tors have been the subject of much debate in geomorphology, both from the point of view of their origin and the implications of this for landscape development in general. Two main hypotheses have been proposed. The first envisages a period of deep chemical weathering of the bedrock possibly during warmer climates of the Tertiary (Figure 11a). An irregular contact between the debris mantle and fresh rock is produced by variations in the depth of weathering as determined by the degree of jointing or rock susceptibility to the processes of decomposition. Subsequently the weathered mantle is removed by water erosion or mass movements leaving relatively unweathered

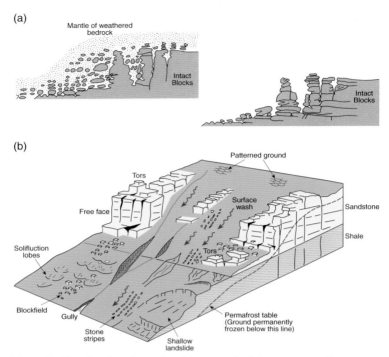

Figure 11: Theories of tor formation: (a) as a result of the emergence of intact
blocks from a mantle of weathered bedrock, and (b) through the retreat of a free face
under periglacial conditions.

rock as upstanding tors. A second hypothesis (Figure 11b) sees tors in
Britain as merely one of a group of features produced under cold
climate conditions. It is thought that tors are isolated by severe freeze-
thaw activity from retreating scarp edges with solifluctional mass
movement removing the shattered debris. Such a process is also seen
as being responsible for the formation of hillslope benches or terraces
in some areas.

Hathersage Moor (SK 255813) is a good location in which to view
many of the features associated with tor landscapes (Figure 12a). The
moor forms a spur projecting west from the main Derwent Edge and
lies west of Burbage Brook, a tributary of the River Derwent (Figure
10). The rocks of Hathersage Moor dip east and south-east and are cut
by several faults in approximately the direction of the dip (Figure
12a). As a result, the Chatsworth or Rivelin Grit occurs in several
downfaulted outcrops bounded by free faces, giving the moor a
stepped character. Associated with these outcrops are the main tor
groups. The most northerly of these, Higger Tor (SK 257820), is a
large mass with a rounded form showing strong signs of
disintegration. Its upper part is composed of detached blocks. To the
south-east and south-west lie Carl Wark (SK 259815) (Photo 14) and
Winyards Nick (SK 252812); the former surmounted by an Iron Age

Photo 14: Carl Wark. Photo: Roger Dalton.

fort and again constituting a large tor mass. The southernmost and lowest outcrop of Chatsworth Grit, Mother Cap Moor (SK 252805), contains eight small but distinct tors.

The tors of Mother Cap Moor vary in size, shape and position. Over Owler Tor (SK 252808) and Mother Cap (Figure 12b) itself are the largest of the group being about 8m in height. Over Owler Tor, perched on a quarried free face on the north-western edge of the Moor, is split by widened vertical joints and heavily weathered sub-horizontal bedding planes into a series of blocks. In contrast, Mother Cap comprises a distinctive cuboid shape with sides 8-10m and forms an isolated mass of cross-bedded sandstone on the west central side of the moor. Both these tors demonstrate the importance of lines of weakness, such as jointing, in the determination of the form of tors. The remaining unnamed tors lie around the periphery of Mother Cap Moor, usually in close proximity to free face scarps. They are small, ranging in height from 3 to 4m. Tor B (Figure 12b) is the smallest in plan size with a maximum width at the base of 3m. It also has a distinctive 'cheese-ring' shape with progressively smaller tabular blocks resting on each other. This contrasts with Tor A which has a pronounced tabular shape. The other tors have a near-regular cuboid form, though their detailed outline is influenced by preferential exploitation of bedding planes. In addition to these small tors, isolated detached blocks also occur. Evidence of contemporary weathering activity is to be found on many of the tors in the form of pan holes. Over Owler Tor and Tor C show good examples of these features about 50cm in diameter and 20cm deep, but on other tors hollows reach 1m in diameter and 50cm in depth. Several of the tors also display varying amounts of undercutting with overhangs up to 1m.

Areas of bare rock are exposed over Mother Cap Moor which may represent the bases or plinths of former tors. Such plinths are

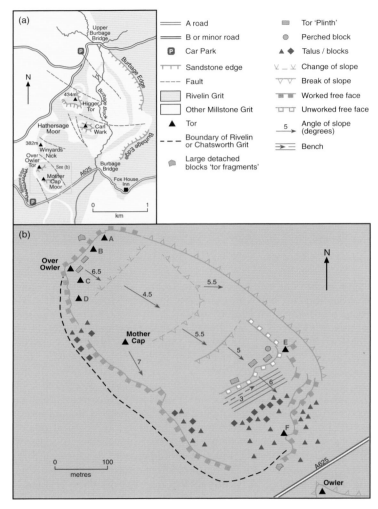

Figure 12: *(a) Burbage Edge and Hathersage Moor, and (b) geomorphological features of the Mother Cap Moor area.*

especially common in the vicinity of free face scars which cross the moor and also occur on the scarp crest east of Over Owler Tor (Figure 12b). Removal of tor blocks from these plinths may have resulted from undercutting followed by toppling.

The free face scarps are also a significant feature of Mother Cap Moor. The western, north-western and south-eastern sides are bounded by free faces which have been extensively quarried. Other unworked rock edges which cross the southern half of Mother Cap Moor are aligned along the strike of the bedrock. These scarps are low, rarely exceeding 3m in height, and in places are breached and shattered. They are separated by benches between 80m and 100m wide which incline downslope at angles slightly in excess of the overall moor slope of about 5°. The benches also have a slope to the east of approximately 3° (Figure 12b).

Such features have been described from the upper Derwent basin and other parts of Britain (see Goudie, 1990) and are thought to result from periglacial slope planation involving scarp retreat. Supporting evidence for this is the extent to which the bench surfaces and adjacent slopes are littered with angular sandstone blocks. The blocks may be up to 4m across and partly buried in peat. Such material probably represents the rock chiselled from the free faces by frost action together with the dislodged fragments of former tors all of which have been rafted downslope by solifluction. The dating of such activity is problematic, but in the valley of Burbage Brook two head deposits were identified with an intervening soil horizon dated to 11 590-11 360 years BP. This would suggest that at least some of the features of Mother Cap Moor were being sculpted in the late Devensian period.

Mother Cap Moor provides a good opportunity to observe many of the features of a tor landscape in a small area. Whilst much of the evidence would seem to point to a Pleistocene periglacial origin for the features of the Moor, it is impossible to dismiss the two-stage tor hypothesis entirely since some 'preparation' of land surfaces will have occurred prior to, and in between, periglacial phases. Both warm and cold climate phases in the Quaternary lasted for many thousands of years, so weathering and erosion during these periods may have played some part in tor production. Furthermore, recent studies in other parts of Britain (Goudie, 1990) have provided fresh evidence for the possible survival of Tertiary weathering profiles. In the post-glacial period weathering and erosion may have caused rounding of some rock surfaces. Peat formation has clothed much rock debris but this is now being removed.

Access

The tors of Hathersage Moor can be approached either from the A625 or the minor road from the A625 at Hathersage Booths to Ringinglow (SK 257826). A small car park at Surprise View (SK 251801) on the A625 lies just south of Mother Cap Moor and from here paths provide routes to the larger tors of Higger Tor and Carl Wark as well as to Mother Cap itself. Off-road parking by the minor road at Upper Burbage Bridge (SK 259829) is limited but is closer to Higger Tor. Good views of Mother Cap Moor are provided along the B6521 road between the A625 and the B6001.

THE
ASHOVER ANTICLINE

Although just outside the confines of the National Park boundary, the village of Ashover is situated amidst classic Peak District scenery on the eastern limb of the main Pennine upfold (Figure 2a, page 7). Here the River Amber has cut deeply into a localised anticlinal flexure to reveal a core of Dinantian limestones with marginal outcrops of Namurian shales and sandstones (Figure 13b). The limestones give rise to a slightly elevated central area of land not exceeding 200m OD. This is separated by lower-lying shale vales from the characteristic moorland terrain of the surrounding gritstone uplands which rise to over 300m OD. Immediately to the north-east and south-west of Ashover village, the limestone inlier is overlooked by prominent edges of resistant sandstone. With their fractured and weathered free faces and capping of tors, these edges are reminiscent of the more extensive gritstone escarpments found elsewhere in the Dark Peak. Thus within a relatively small area around Ashover many of the features representative of the Peak District as a whole may be seen. In essence this is a Peak District in miniature: a microcosm that encapsulates the regional structure, rock types and landforms.

In broad terms the Ashover Anticline takes the form of an elongated dome or **pericline** in which the rocks show a tendency to dip outwards in all directions from a central position on the north-west to south-east trending axis. However, a perfect domal structure is not achieved because the feature is really only a high point on the undulating crest line of a more extensive anticlinal fold which interrupts the general easterly inclination of the Carboniferous rocks hereabouts. Another undulation causes the limestones to be exposed again as a separate inlier around Crich (SK 350545), some 8km further south. Here, as at Ashover (SK 358632), a rock succession extending from the Dinantian to the Westphalian is encountered within a relatively short distance.

The anticlinal structure at Ashover is particularly notable because its reflection in the landscape is so clearly apparent in the field. At the same time, it provides a classic example of inverted relief. The River Amber has incised its course along the axial surface trace of the Ashover Anticline where it has been able to exploit a sequence of relatively unresistant volcanic ashes (tuff) present within the limestones (Figure 13b). Thus the former crest line of the fold is now represented by a deep valley whereas the limbs have been accentuated by erosion to form inward facing scarp slopes which dominate the local scenery. In contrast, at Crich, it is the limestone core which is prominent in the landscape while the surrounding sandstones do not

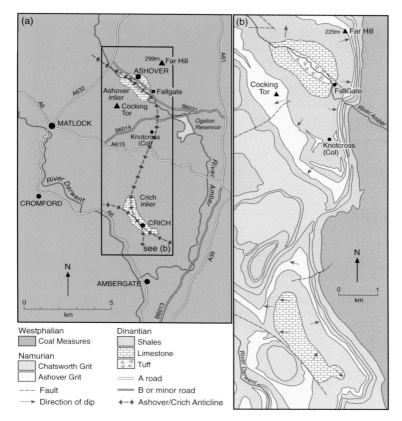

Figure 13: Ashover and Crich (a) the lower Derwent Valley, and (b) detail of geological features.

give rise to conspicuous features. This is partly because the Crich Anticline has not been significantly dissected by streams, and partly because the Namurian outcrop on the south-western side of the fold has been downfaulted.

There is little doubt that the River Amber has played a significant role in the development of the distinctive relief at Ashover. Nevertheless, its route across the Ashover Anticline is anomalous and not easy to explain. It is tempting to invoke superimposition of the river from a presumed former cover of Mesozoic rocks. Even so, it would be a remarkable coincidence if such superimposition had occurred directly over the crest of an anticline in the Carboniferous rocks below. It is possible, of course, that the crest of the Ashover Anticline was weakened by the preferential development of tension joints which facilitated erosion in this area. However, the structural trend of the fold and the course taken by the River Amber do not match up entirely. Near Fallgate (SK 355621) the axial surface trace of the Ashover Anticline changes to a north to south alignment whereas the river continues on its south-easterly course. Thus, downstream of Fallgate the River Amber becomes markedly discordant as it cuts obliquely across the strike of the Namurian outcrop and flows south-eastwards on to the (Westphalian) Coal Measures.

If the River Amber was superimposed on the Ashover Anticline, it would appear that it cut down into the limestone core without any tendency to shift laterally on the less resistant shales. However, it is possible that lateral migration was effectively prevented by large-scale mass movement from the surrounding gritstone edges during episodes of intense periglacial weathering. Some evidence to support this view is found in the thick sheets of solifluction debris (head) which now cloak the lower scarp slopes and the shale vales. With such periglacial modification of the landscape, it is difficult to establish whether the River Amber has always escaped from the Ashover Anticline by means of the discordant exit near Fallgate, or whether the river originally followed the shale outcrop and flowed further south through the col at Knotcross on the B6014 east of Butterley (SK 355605). The Knotcross col lies along the axial surface trace of the fold and could represent the degraded section of an abandoned river valley (Figure 13b). Alternatively it might merely be a wind gap formed as a result of normal slope recession away from the fold axis. In any event, the reason for the existing discordant exit from the Ashover Anticline is puzzling.

An unknown factor in any interpretation of landscape evolution at Ashover is the effect of glacial erosion. Ice moving towards the south-east could have removed the sandstone capping of the Ashover Anticline and preferentially eroded the underlying shales. This would have created a linear depression and facilitated the development of a river valley. Following the same line of reasoning, it can be suggested that a sub-glacial stream might have been responsible for the anomalous breach in the gritstone escarpment near Fallgate. Glacial deposits do occur along the general line of the Amber Valley north-west of Ashover, and also further south around Crich.

Careful study of the landscape around Ashover thus reveals many problems of interpretation that are typical of other parts of the Peak District. The broad relationship between rocks and relief is apparent almost everywhere. However, the evolution of the drainage pattern is much less clear. While there can be little doubt that late Pleistocene glacial and periglacial episodes significantly influenced the development of landforms, the overall effect of such activity is difficult to assess. In order to clarify this issue, landform studies need to be supported by detailed investigation of associated Pleistocene sediments. There is a major need for further work of this type, both at Ashover and in the Peak District as a whole.

Access
The Ashover Anticline can be conveniently explored on foot by means of a north-east to south-west transect from Farhill (SK 358636)

to Cocking Tor (SK 344616). Both locations offer excellent vantage points from which to view the local structure and scenery, and footpaths lead down towards the valley floor and Ashover village. There is a limited amount of room for parking cars on minor roads at each end of the transect route via the B6036 for Farhill, and the A632 or the B6014 for Cocking Tor, and also in Ashover village at SK 348633.

GLOSSARY

Anticline. A rock sequence which has been upfolded.

Blockfield. Continuous surface spread of periglacially weathered blocks, often at the foot of slopes.

BP. Years before the present.

Cuesta. A landform developed by differential erosion on gently dipping strata comprising a steep scarp face and a less steeply inclined dip slope.

Dendritic. A drainage pattern which is branching or tree-like in plan.

Differential erosion. Where erosion is selective in attacking weaker rocks.

Drumlinoid. In the form of elongated mounds like drumlins.

Free face. A near-vertical rock exposure.

Head. An accumulation of poorly sorted debris formed under freeze-thaw conditions in a periglacial environment.

Lithology. The general character of a rock, particularly as seen in field exposures and hand specimens.

Mass movement. The movement of weathered material downslope *en masse.*

Meltwater. The water which is derived from the melting of glaciers, ice sheets and snow patches.

OD. Ordnance Datum; mean sea-level at Newlyn, Cornwall. From this level all heights on British maps are calculated.

Outcrop. The occurrence of rock at the Earth's surface.

Pericline. A short anticline which pitches in all directions from a point along its axis in the manner of an elongated dome.

Periglacial. Term describing a cold climate environment characteristic of the margins of ice-sheets and glaciers.

Pore pressure. The pressure exerted on particles within soil and rocks by water contained within voids.

Regolith. The mantle of unconsolidated material, whatever its nature or origin.

Slopewash. The removal of material across a slope by surface runoff.

Strike. The direction at right angles to the dip of inclined strata.

Superimposed. Of a drainage pattern developed conformably with one geological structure, then lowered by erosion onto an underlying structure.

Syncline. A rock sequence which has been downfolded.

Till. The ill-sorted debris deposited by an ice sheet or glacier.

Tor. A conspicuous upstanding rock outcrop on a hillslope or hill top.

BIBLIOGRAPHY

Aitkenhead, N., Chisholm, J.I. and Stevenson, I.P. (1985) 'Geology of the country around Buxton, Leek and Bakewell', *Memoirs of the British Geological Survey*, Sheet 111, London: HMSO.

Burek, C.V. (1991) 'Quaternary history and glacial deposits of the Peak District' in Ehlers, J., Gibbard, P.L. and Rose, J. (eds) *Glacial Deposits in Great Britain and Ireland*. Rotterdam: Balkema, pp. 193-201.

Catalogues of BGS's maps, books and other publications are available on request from: Sales Desk, British Geological Survey, Kingsley Dunham Centre, Keyworth, Nottingham NG12 5GG. Tel: 0115 936 3241; Fax: 0115 936 3488.

Cunningham, F.F. (1964) 'A detail of process on scarp edges of Millstone Grit', *East Midlands Geographer*, 3, pp. 322-325.

Cunningham, F.F. (1965) 'Tor theories in the light of South Pennine evidence', *East Midlands Geographer*, 3, pp. 424-433.

Dalton, R., Fox, H. and Jones, P. (1999) *Classic Landforms of the White Peak*. Sheffield: Geographical Association.

Doornkamp, J.C. (1990) 'Landslides in Derbyshire', *East Midlands Geographer*, 13, pp. 33-62.

Goudie, A. (1990) *The Landforms of England and Wales*. Oxford: Blackwell.

Jowett, A. and Charlesworth, J.K. (1929) 'On the glacial geology of the Derbyshire dome and the western slopes of the southern Pennines', *Quarterly Journal of the Geological Society*, 85, pp. 307-34.

Johnson, R.H., Tallis, J.H. and Wilson, P. (1990) 'The Seal Edge Coombes, North Derbyshire', *Journal of Quaternary Science*, 5, pp. 83-94.

Johnson R.H. and Vaughan R.D. (1983) 'The Alport Castles, Derbyshire: a south Pennine slope and its geomorphic history', *East Midlands Geographer*, 8, pp. 37-52.

Stevenson, I.P. and Gaunt, G.D. (1971) 'Geology of the country around Chapel-en-le-Frith', *Memoirs of the British Geological Survey*, Sheet 99, London: HMSO.

Steward, H.E. and Cripps, J.E. (1983) 'Some engineering implications of the chemical weathering of pyritic shell', *Quarterly Journal of Engineering Geology*, 16, p. 281.

Tallis, J.H. (1985) 'Mass movement and erosion of a southern Pennine blanket peat', *Journal of Ecology*, 73, pp. 283-315.

Wilson, P. (1981) 'Periglacial valley fill sediments at Edale, North Derbyshire', *East Midlands Geographer*, 5, pp. 263-271.